Raintree is an imprint of Capstone Global
Library Limited, a company incorporated in
England and Wales having its registered office
at 264 Banbury Road, Oxford, OX2 7DY –
Registered company number: 6695582

www.raintree.co.uk
myorders@raintree.co.uk

ISBN 978 1 4747 6660 9
22 21 20 19 18
10 9 8 7 6 5 4 3 2 1

British Library Cataloguing in Publication Data
A full catalogue record for this book is available
from the British Library.

Editorial: Chris Harbo and Gena Chester
Design: Hilary Wacholz
Production: Kris Wilfahrt
Originated by Capstone Global Library Ltd
Printed and bound in India

Superman created by Jerry Siegel and Joe
Shuster. By special arrangement with the
Jerry Siegel family.

SUPER POWERS!™

Dark Knight Dilemma!

BY ART BALTAZAR AND FRANCO

raintree
a Capstone company — publishers for children

MEANWHILE, ON THE ISLAND OF THEMYSCIRA...

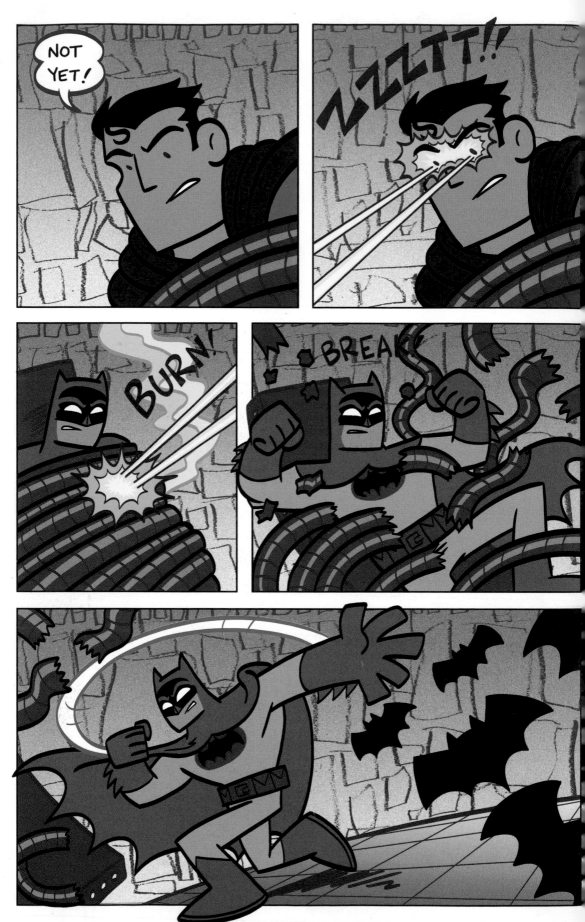

CREATORS

ART BALTAZAR IS A CARTOONIST MACHINE FROM THE HEART OF CHICAGO! HE DEFINES CARTOONS AND COMICS NOT ONLY AS AN ART STYLE, BUT AS A WAY OF LIFE. CURRENTLY, ART IS THE CREATIVE FORCE BEHIND *THE NEW YORK TIMES* BEST-SELLING, EISNER AWARD-WINNING DC COMICS SERIES TINY TITANS, THE CO-WRITER FOR *BILLY BATSON AND THE MAGIC OF SHAZAM!*, AND CO-CREATOR OF SUPERMAN FAMILY ADVENTURES. ART IS LIVING THE DREAM! HE DRAWS COMICS AND NEVER HAS TO LEAVE THE HOUSE. HE LIVES WITH HIS LOVELY WIFE, ROSE, "BIG BOY" SONNY, LITTLE BOY GORDON AND LITTLE GIRL AUDREY. RIGHT ON!

ART BALTAZAR

FRANCO

FRANCO AURELIANI, BRONX, NEW YORK, BORN WRITER AND ARTIST, HAS BEEN DRAWING COMICS SINCE HE COULD HOLD A CRAYON. CURRENTLY RESIDING IN UPSTATE NEW YORK WITH HIS WIFE, IVETTE, AND SON, NICOLAS, FRANCO SPENDS MOST OF HIS DAYS IN A BATCAVE-LIKE STUDIO WHERE HE HAS PRODUCED DC'S TINY TITANS COMICS. IN 1995, FRANCO FOUNDED BLINDWOLF STUDIOS, AN INDEPENDENT ART STUDIO WHERE HE AND FELLOW CREATORS CAN CREATE CHILDREN'S COMICS. FRANCO IS THE CREATOR, ARTIST, AND WRITER OF *PATRICK THE WOLF BOY*. WHEN HE'S NOT WRITING AND DRAWING, FRANCO ALSO TEACHES HIGH SCHOOL ART.

GLOSSARY

delusional be mistaken, or have misleading beliefs

destruction what happens when something is destroyed

DNA material in cells that gives people their individual characteristics; DNA stands for deoxyribonucleic acid

encrypted when information has been hidden with a secret code or cypher

enlarge make something bigger

fortress building or place that is strengthened against attack

lure draw someone or something in with a fake reward

manipulate change something in a clever way to influence people to do or think what you want

mastermind main planner, or the original source of a plot

miniature much smaller than usual size

peril danger

solitude be alone

technology use of science to do practical things such as designing complex machines

traitor someone who helps the enemy of their allies

warped something becoming bent or twisted over time

witness person who has seen or heard something

VISUAL QUESTIONS AND WRITING PROMPTS

1. RE-READ PAGES 10 AND 11. WHY DO YOU THINK THE RIDDLER HELPS SUPERMAN IN THESE PANELS?

2. LOOK AT THE FACIAL EXPRESSIONS BELOW. WHAT DO THEY TELL YOU ABOUT LIFE ON NEW KRYPTON?

3. IMAGINE SUPERMAN'S PARENTS TALK TO BRAINIAC AFTER THE EVENTS IN THIS BOOK. WRITE DOWN THEIR CONVERSATION.

4. BRAINIAC IS SUPERMAN'S HALF-BROTHER IN THIS STORY. WHAT SIMILARITIES CAN YOU SEE BETWEEN THE TWO? WHAT DIFFERENCES?

READ THEM ALL!